THE Reading Woman
ADDRESS BOOK

Pomegranate
PORTLAND, OREGON

Published by Pomegranate Communications, Inc.

19018 NE Portal Way, Portland OR 97230

800 227 1428; www.pomegranate.com

Pomegranate Europe Ltd.

Unit 1, Heathcote Business Centre, Hurlbutt Road

Warwick, Warwickshire CV34 6TD, UK

[+44] 0 1926 430111; sales@pomeurope.co.uk

Conceived by Maxine Rose Schur

COVER: Valentine Cameron Prinsep (English, 1838–1904)
Lady Tennyson on Afton Downs, Freshwater Bay, Isle of Wight, n.d.
Private collection
© Mallett Gallery, London / The Bridgeman Art Library, New York

Pomegranate Catalog No. AA413

ISBN 978-0-7649-4181-8

Designed by Ronni Madrid

Printed in Korea

23 22 21 20 19 18 17 16 15 14   12 11 10 9 8 7 6 5 4 3

She is finding escape from routine in the pages of a novel. Or searching the pages of a more serious work for a way to broaden her horizons or transform her life. Or poring over a letter from a loved one. The reading woman represents a long, complex story that has fascinated generations of artists.

A book can stop time, transcend circumstances, conjure a world in which to lose oneself. The forty paintings in this address book achieve the same thing. Just as the reading woman has temporarily set herself free from her life's narrative, so can we leave ours as we contemplate her image.

Why has the reading woman been such a popular subject for painters through the ages? Beyond being beautiful in herself, she is an expression of important, unspoken cultural ideas. She is ensconced in comfortable surroundings; she is at leisure: all's right with the world. And that she is using her leisure to read implies that she is cultured—the further implication being that the painter, too, is a person of culture. The reading woman is a confirmation and a celebration of quiet comfort and hard-earned social stability.

If you love words, the impulse to share words of your own, on the subject of your love, is strong. Well-chosen observations on the pleasures of literature, from historical and contemporary readers and writers, accompany each of the images presented here.

Julius Leblanc Stewart (American, 1855–1919)
Sarah Bernhardt (1844–1923) and Christine Nilsson (1843–1921), n.d.
Oil on canvas
Private collection
© Christie's Images, London / The Bridgeman Art Library, New York

There is no Frigate like a Book
To take us Lands away,
Nor any Coursers like a Page
Of prancing Poetry.
　　　　—Emily Dickinson (1830–1886)

Stuart G. Davis (English, fl. 1893–1904)

A Good Book, n.d.

Oil on panel, 39.6 x 29.9 cm (15⅝ x 11¾ in.)

Private collection

Photograph courtesy Manya Igel Fine Arts Ltd., London / The Bridgeman Art Library, New York

A book is a garden, an orchard, a storehouse, a party,
a company by the way, a counselor, a multitude of counselors.

—Henry Ward Beecher (1813–1887)

NAME	PHONE (H)
ADDRESS	PHONE (W)
	FAX
EMAIL	CELL/PAGER

NAME	PHONE (H)
ADDRESS	PHONE (W)
	FAX
EMAIL	CELL/PAGER

NAME	PHONE (H)
ADDRESS	PHONE (W)
	FAX
EMAIL	CELL/PAGER

NAME	PHONE (H)
ADDRESS	PHONE (W)
	FAX
EMAIL	CELL/PAGER

NAME	PHONE (H)
ADDRESS	PHONE (W)
	FAX
EMAIL	CELL/PAGER

NAME	PHONE (H)
ADDRESS	PHONE (W)
	FAX
EMAIL	CELL/PAGER

NAME	PHONE (H)
ADDRESS	PHONE (W)
	FAX
EMAIL	CELL/PAGER

NAME	PHONE (H)
ADDRESS	PHONE (W)
	FAX
EMAIL	CELL/PAGER

NAME	PHONE (H)
ADDRESS	PHONE (W)
	FAX
EMAIL	CELL/PAGER

NAME	PHONE (H)
ADDRESS	PHONE (W)
	FAX
EMAIL	CELL/PAGER

NAME	PHONE (H)
ADDRESS	PHONE (W)
	FAX
EMAIL	CELL/PAGER

NAME	PHONE (H)
ADDRESS	PHONE (W)
	FAX
EMAIL	CELL/PAGER

NAME	PHONE (H)
ADDRESS	PHONE (W)
	FAX
EMAIL	CELL/PAGER

NAME	PHONE (H)
ADDRESS	PHONE (W)
	FAX
EMAIL	CELL/PAGER

NAME	PHONE (H)
ADDRESS	PHONE (W)
	FAX
EMAIL	CELL/PAGER

NAME	PHONE (H)
ADDRESS	PHONE (W)
	FAX
EMAIL	CELL/PAGER

NAME	PHONE (H)
ADDRESS	PHONE (W)
	FAX
EMAIL	CELL/PAGER

NAME	PHONE (H)
ADDRESS	PHONE (W)
	FAX
EMAIL	CELL/PAGER

NAME

ADDRESS

EMAIL

PHONE (H)

PHONE (W)

FAX

CELL/PAGER

NAME

ADDRESS

EMAIL

PHONE (H)

PHONE (W)

FAX

CELL/PAGER

NAME

ADDRESS

EMAIL

PHONE (H)

PHONE (W)

FAX

CELL/PAGER

NAME

ADDRESS

EMAIL

PHONE (H)

PHONE (W)

FAX

CELL/PAGER

NAME

ADDRESS

EMAIL

PHONE (H)

PHONE (W)

FAX

CELL/PAGER

NAME

ADDRESS

EMAIL

PHONE (H)

PHONE (W)

FAX

CELL/PAGER

August Macke (German, 1887–1914)
Elisabeth Reading, n.d.
Pfalzgalerie, Kaiserslautern, Germany
Photograph courtesy The Bridgeman Art Library, New York

I only read what I am hungry for at the moment when I have an appetite for it, and then I do not read, I eat.
—Simone Weil, *Waiting for God* (1950)

Ambrosius Benson (Dutch, 1495–1550)
Young Woman Reading a Book of Hours, n.d.
Oil on panel
Musée du Louvre, Paris
Photograph courtesy Peter Willi / The Bridgeman Art Library, New York

'Tis the good reader that makes the good book.
—Ralph Waldo Emerson (1803–1882)

NAME		PHONE (H)
ADDRESS		PHONE (W)
		FAX
EMAIL		CELL/PAGER

NAME		PHONE (H)
ADDRESS		PHONE (W)
		FAX
EMAIL		CELL/PAGER

NAME		PHONE (H)
ADDRESS		PHONE (W)
		FAX
EMAIL		CELL/PAGER

NAME		PHONE (H)
ADDRESS		PHONE (W)
		FAX
EMAIL		CELL/PAGER

NAME		PHONE (H)
ADDRESS		PHONE (W)
		FAX
EMAIL		CELL/PAGER

NAME		PHONE (H)
ADDRESS		PHONE (W)
		FAX
EMAIL		CELL/PAGER

NAME	PHONE (H)
ADDRESS	PHONE (W)
	FAX
EMAIL	CELL/PAGER

NAME	PHONE (H)
ADDRESS	PHONE (W)
	FAX
EMAIL	CELL/PAGER

NAME	PHONE (H)
ADDRESS	PHONE (W)
	FAX
EMAIL	CELL/PAGER

NAME	PHONE (H)
ADDRESS	PHONE (W)
	FAX
EMAIL	CELL/PAGER

NAME	PHONE (H)
ADDRESS	PHONE (W)
	FAX
EMAIL	CELL/PAGER

NAME	PHONE (H)
ADDRESS	PHONE (W)
	FAX
EMAIL	CELL/PAGER

NAME	PHONE (H)
ADDRESS	PHONE (W)
	FAX
EMAIL	CELL/PAGER

NAME	PHONE (H)
ADDRESS	PHONE (W)
	FAX
EMAIL	CELL/PAGER

NAME	PHONE (H)
ADDRESS	PHONE (W)
	FAX
EMAIL	CELL/PAGER

NAME	PHONE (H)
ADDRESS	PHONE (W)
	FAX
EMAIL	CELL/PAGER

NAME	PHONE (H)
ADDRESS	PHONE (W)
	FAX
EMAIL	CELL/PAGER

NAME	PHONE (H)
ADDRESS	PHONE (W)
	FAX
EMAIL	CELL/PAGER

NAME	PHONE (H)
ADDRESS	PHONE (W)
	FAX
EMAIL	CELL/PAGER

NAME	PHONE (H)
ADDRESS	PHONE (W)
	FAX
EMAIL	CELL/PAGER

NAME	PHONE (H)
ADDRESS	PHONE (W)
	FAX
EMAIL	CELL/PAGER

NAME	PHONE (H)
ADDRESS	PHONE (W)
	FAX
EMAIL	CELL/PAGER

NAME	PHONE (H)
ADDRESS	PHONE (W)
	FAX
EMAIL	CELL/PAGER

NAME	PHONE (H)
ADDRESS	PHONE (W)
	FAX
EMAIL	CELL/PAGER

NAME	PHONE (H)
ADDRESS	PHONE (W)
	FAX
EMAIL	CELL/PAGER

NAME	PHONE (H)
ADDRESS	PHONE (W)
	FAX
EMAIL	CELL/PAGER

NAME	PHONE (H)
ADDRESS	PHONE (W)
	FAX
EMAIL	CELL/PAGER

NAME	PHONE (H)
ADDRESS	PHONE (W)
	FAX
EMAIL	CELL/PAGER

NAME	PHONE (H)
ADDRESS	PHONE (W)
	FAX
EMAIL	CELL/PAGER

NAME	PHONE (H)
ADDRESS	PHONE (W)
	FAX
EMAIL	CELL/PAGER

NAME	PHONE (H)
ADDRESS	PHONE (W)
	FAX
EMAIL	CELL/PAGER

NAME	PHONE (H)
ADDRESS	PHONE (W)
	FAX
EMAIL	CELL/PAGER

NAME	PHONE (H)
ADDRESS	PHONE (W)
	FAX
EMAIL	CELL/PAGER

NAME	PHONE (H)
ADDRESS	PHONE (W)
	FAX
EMAIL	CELL/PAGER

NAME	PHONE (H)
ADDRESS	PHONE (W)
	FAX
EMAIL	CELL/PAGER

NAME	PHONE (H)
ADDRESS	PHONE (W)
	FAX
EMAIL	CELL/PAGER

Master of Oberrheinischer (German, fifteenth century)
Garden of Paradise, c. 1415
Tempera on panel
Städelsches Kunstinstitut, Frankfurt-am-Main, Germany
Photograph courtesy The Bridgeman Art Library, New York

> *The pleasure of all reading is doubled when one lives with another who shares the same books.*
> —Katherine Mansfield, in John Middleton Murry, ed., *The Letters of Katherine Mansfield* (1928)

George Smith (English, 1829–1901)

Dreaming of Her Lover, 1868

Oil on panel, 50.8 x 43.2 cm (20 x 17 in.)

Private collection / Haynes Fine Art at the Bindery Galleries, Broadway

Photograph courtesy The Bridgeman Art Library, New York

The poem has a social effect of some kind whether or not the poet wills that it have. It has kinetic force,
it sets in motion . . . elements in the reader that would otherwise be stagnant.
—Denise Levertov, *"A Testament and a Postscript," in* The Poet in the World *(1973)*

NAME	PHONE (H)
ADDRESS	PHONE (W)
	FAX
EMAIL	CELL/PAGER

NAME	PHONE (H)
ADDRESS	PHONE (W)
	FAX
EMAIL	CELL/PAGER

NAME	PHONE (H)
ADDRESS	PHONE (W)
	FAX
EMAIL	CELL/PAGER

NAME	PHONE (H)
ADDRESS	PHONE (W)
	FAX
EMAIL	CELL/PAGER

NAME	PHONE (H)
ADDRESS	PHONE (W)
	FAX
EMAIL	CELL/PAGER

NAME	PHONE (H)
ADDRESS	PHONE (W)
	FAX
EMAIL	CELL/PAGER

NAME	PHONE (H)
ADDRESS	PHONE (W)
	FAX
EMAIL	CELL/PAGER

NAME	PHONE (H)
ADDRESS	PHONE (W)
	FAX
EMAIL	CELL/PAGER

NAME	PHONE (H)
ADDRESS	PHONE (W)
	FAX
EMAIL	CELL/PAGER

NAME	PHONE (H)
ADDRESS	PHONE (W)
	FAX
EMAIL	CELL/PAGER

NAME	PHONE (H)
ADDRESS	PHONE (W)
	FAX
EMAIL	CELL/PAGER

NAME	PHONE (H)
ADDRESS	PHONE (W)
	FAX
EMAIL	CELL/PAGER

NAME	PHONE (H)
ADDRESS	PHONE (W)
	FAX
EMAIL	CELL/PAGER

NAME	PHONE (H)
ADDRESS	PHONE (W)
	FAX
EMAIL	CELL/PAGER

NAME	PHONE (H)
ADDRESS	PHONE (W)
	FAX
EMAIL	CELL/PAGER

NAME	PHONE (H)
ADDRESS	PHONE (W)
	FAX
EMAIL	CELL/PAGER

NAME	PHONE (H)
ADDRESS	PHONE (W)
	FAX
EMAIL	CELL/PAGER

NAME	PHONE (H)
ADDRESS	PHONE (W)
	FAX
EMAIL	CELL/PAGER

NAME

ADDRESS

EMAIL

PHONE (H)

PHONE (W)

FAX

CELL/PAGER

NAME

ADDRESS

EMAIL

PHONE (H)

PHONE (W)

FAX

CELL/PAGER

NAME

ADDRESS

EMAIL

PHONE (H)

PHONE (W)

FAX

CELL/PAGER

NAME

ADDRESS

EMAIL

PHONE (H)

PHONE (W)

FAX

CELL/PAGER

NAME

ADDRESS

EMAIL

PHONE (H)

PHONE (W)

FAX

CELL/PAGER

NAME

ADDRESS

EMAIL

PHONE (H)

PHONE (W)

FAX

CELL/PAGER

Marianne Stokes (English, 1855–1927)
A Slovak Woman at Prayer, Vazcecz, Hungary, 1907
Gouache on paper, 27.3 x 32.3 cm (10¾ x 12¾ in.)
Private collection
Photograph courtesy The Bridgeman Art Library, New York

When I only begin to read, I forget I'm on this world. It lifts me on wings with high thoughts.
—Anzia Yezierska, "Wings," *Hungry Hearts* (1920)

Sir Edward Burne-Jones (English, 1833–1898)
Winter, 1869–1870
Gouache on paper
Photograph courtesy Roy Miles Fine Paintings, London / The
Bridgeman Art Library, New York

I easily sink into mere absorption of what other minds have done, and should like a whole life for that alone.
—George Eliot, in J. W. Cross, ed., *George Eliot's Life as Related in Her Letters and Journals* (1884)

NAME

ADDRESS

EMAIL

PHONE (H)

PHONE (W)

FAX

CELL/PAGER

NAME

ADDRESS

EMAIL

PHONE (H)

PHONE (W)

FAX

CELL/PAGER

NAME

ADDRESS

EMAIL

PHONE (H)

PHONE (W)

FAX

CELL/PAGER

NAME

ADDRESS

EMAIL

PHONE (H)

PHONE (W)

FAX

CELL/PAGER

NAME

ADDRESS

EMAIL

PHONE (H)

PHONE (W)

FAX

CELL/PAGER

NAME

ADDRESS

EMAIL

PHONE (H)

PHONE (W)

FAX

CELL/PAGER

NAME	PHONE (H)
ADDRESS	PHONE (W)
	FAX
EMAIL	CELL/PAGER

NAME	PHONE (H)
ADDRESS	PHONE (W)
	FAX
EMAIL	CELL/PAGER

NAME	PHONE (H)
ADDRESS	PHONE (W)
	FAX
EMAIL	CELL/PAGER

NAME	PHONE (H)
ADDRESS	PHONE (W)
	FAX
EMAIL	CELL/PAGER

NAME	PHONE (H)
ADDRESS	PHONE (W)
	FAX
EMAIL	CELL/PAGER

NAME	PHONE (H)
ADDRESS	PHONE (W)
	FAX
EMAIL	CELL/PAGER

Edward Killingworth Johnson (English, 1825–1923)

Summertime: Portrait of the Artist's Wife, Hannah, n.d.

Watercolor and gouache on paper, 48.8 x 35.5 cm (19¼ x 13¹⁵⁄₁₆ in.)
John Spink Fine Watercolours, London
Photograph courtesy The Bridgeman Art Library, New York

Fiction is like a spider's web, attached ever so lightly perhaps, but still attached to life at all four corners.
—Virginia Woolf

James Jacques Joseph Tissot (French, 1836–1902)

Reading a Book, n.d.

Oil on canvas

Private collection

© Christie's Images, London / The Bridgeman Art Library, New York

*I think I may boast myself to be, with all possible vanity, the most unlearned
and uninformed female who ever dared to be an authoress.*

—Jane Austen

NAME

ADDRESS

EMAIL

PHONE (H)

PHONE (W)

FAX

CELL/PAGER

NAME

ADDRESS

EMAIL

PHONE (H)

PHONE (W)

FAX

CELL/PAGER

NAME

ADDRESS

EMAIL

PHONE (H)

PHONE (W)

FAX

CELL/PAGER

NAME

ADDRESS

EMAIL

PHONE (H)

PHONE (W)

FAX

CELL/PAGER

NAME

ADDRESS

EMAIL

PHONE (H)

PHONE (W)

FAX

CELL/PAGER

NAME

ADDRESS

EMAIL

PHONE (H)

PHONE (W)

FAX

CELL/PAGER

NAME	PHONE (H)
ADDRESS	PHONE (W)
	FAX
EMAIL	CELL/PAGER

NAME	PHONE (H)
ADDRESS	PHONE (W)
	FAX
EMAIL	CELL/PAGER

NAME	PHONE (H)
ADDRESS	PHONE (W)
	FAX
EMAIL	CELL/PAGER

NAME	PHONE (H)
ADDRESS	PHONE (W)
	FAX
EMAIL	CELL/PAGER

NAME	PHONE (H)
ADDRESS	PHONE (W)
	FAX
EMAIL	CELL/PAGER

NAME	PHONE (H)
ADDRESS	PHONE (W)
	FAX
EMAIL	CELL/PAGER

NAME	PHONE (H)
ADDRESS	PHONE (W)
	FAX
EMAIL	CELL/PAGER

NAME	PHONE (H)
ADDRESS	PHONE (W)
	FAX
EMAIL	CELL/PAGER

NAME	PHONE (H)
ADDRESS	PHONE (W)
	FAX
EMAIL	CELL/PAGER

NAME	PHONE (H)
ADDRESS	PHONE (W)
	FAX
EMAIL	CELL/PAGER

NAME	PHONE (H)
ADDRESS	PHONE (W)
	FAX
EMAIL	CELL/PAGER

NAME	PHONE (H)
ADDRESS	PHONE (W)
	FAX
EMAIL	CELL/PAGER

NAME	PHONE (H)
ADDRESS	PHONE (W)
	FAX
EMAIL	CELL/PAGER
NAME	PHONE (H)
ADDRESS	PHONE (W)
	FAX
EMAIL	CELL/PAGER
NAME	PHONE (H)
ADDRESS	PHONE (W)
	FAX
EMAIL	CELL/PAGER
NAME	PHONE (H)
ADDRESS	PHONE (W)
	FAX
EMAIL	CELL/PAGER
NAME	PHONE (H)
ADDRESS	PHONE (W)
	FAX
EMAIL	CELL/PAGER
NAME	PHONE (H)
ADDRESS	PHONE (W)
	FAX
EMAIL	CELL/PAGER

Leon Kamir-Kaufman (Polish, 1872–1933)

Woman Reading, 1921

Pastel on paper, 78.5 x 58.5 cm (30¹⁵⁄₁₆ x 23⅛ in.)
Musée d'Orsay, Paris
Photograph courtesy Giraudon / The Bridgeman Art Library, New York

When I . . . discovered libraries, it was like having Christmas every day.
                                        —Jean Fritz (b. 1915)

Attributed to Thomas Pole (fl. c. 1806)
In the Library, St. James' Square, c. 1805–1806
Watercolor on paper
© Bristol City Museum and Art Gallery / The Bridgeman Art Library, New York

Reading makes immigrants of us all. It takes us away from home,
but more important, it finds homes for us everywhere.
—Hazel Rochman (b. 1938)

NAME	PHONE (H)
ADDRESS	PHONE (W)
	FAX
EMAIL	CELL/PAGER

NAME	PHONE (H)
ADDRESS	PHONE (W)
	FAX
EMAIL	CELL/PAGER

NAME	PHONE (H)
ADDRESS	PHONE (W)
	FAX
EMAIL	CELL/PAGER

NAME	PHONE (H)
ADDRESS	PHONE (W)
	FAX
EMAIL	CELL/PAGER

NAME	PHONE (H)
ADDRESS	PHONE (W)
	FAX
EMAIL	CELL/PAGER

NAME	PHONE (H)
ADDRESS	PHONE (W)
	FAX
EMAIL	CELL/PAGER

NAME	PHONE (H)
ADDRESS	PHONE (W)
	FAX
EMAIL	CELL/PAGER

NAME	PHONE (H)
ADDRESS	PHONE (W)
	FAX
EMAIL	CELL/PAGER

NAME	PHONE (H)
ADDRESS	PHONE (W)
	FAX
EMAIL	CELL/PAGER

NAME	PHONE (H)
ADDRESS	PHONE (W)
	FAX
EMAIL	CELL/PAGER

NAME	PHONE (H)
ADDRESS	PHONE (W)
	FAX
EMAIL	CELL/PAGER

NAME	PHONE (H)
ADDRESS	PHONE (W)
	FAX
EMAIL	CELL/PAGER

NAME	PHONE (H)
ADDRESS	PHONE (W)
	FAX
EMAIL	CELL/PAGER

NAME	PHONE (H)
ADDRESS	PHONE (W)
	FAX
EMAIL	CELL/PAGER

NAME	PHONE (H)
ADDRESS	PHONE (W)
	FAX
EMAIL	CELL/PAGER

NAME	PHONE (H)
ADDRESS	PHONE (W)
	FAX
EMAIL	CELL/PAGER

NAME	PHONE (H)
ADDRESS	PHONE (W)
	FAX
EMAIL	CELL/PAGER

NAME	PHONE (H)
ADDRESS	PHONE (W)
	FAX
EMAIL	CELL/PAGER

NAME	PHONE (H)
ADDRESS	PHONE (W)
	FAX
EMAIL	CELL/PAGER

NAME	PHONE (H)
ADDRESS	PHONE (W)
	FAX
EMAIL	CELL/PAGER

NAME	PHONE (H)
ADDRESS	PHONE (W)
	FAX
EMAIL	CELL/PAGER

NAME	PHONE (H)
ADDRESS	PHONE (W)
	FAX
EMAIL	CELL/PAGER

NAME	PHONE (H)
ADDRESS	PHONE (W)
	FAX
EMAIL	CELL/PAGER

NAME	PHONE (H)
ADDRESS	PHONE (W)
	FAX
EMAIL	CELL/PAGER

Mose Bianchi (Italian, 1836–1893)
Young Woman Reading, n.d.
Oil on canvas, 84 x 65 cm (33¹⁄₁₆ x 25⁵⁄₈ in.)
Pinacoteca di Brera, Milan
Photograph courtesy Alinari / The Bridgeman Art Library, New York

If you put your ear close to a book you can hear it talking. A tiny voice, very small, somewhat like a puppet, asexual.
—Anne Sexton

James Jacques Joseph Tissot (French, 1836–1902)
Reverie: Mrs. Newton Reclining in a Chair, n.d.
Oil on canvas
Private collection
Photograph courtesy The Bridgeman Art Library, New York

It is not the volume of one's reading but the way one reads that rewards one.
Those who run ahead at great speed get no rewards at all. They resemble
those bees that can draw the nectar from flowers only by
lying on them, not by wandering among them.
—Jeanne-Marie Bouvier de la Motte Guyon,
Le moyen court et très facile de faire oraison
[The short and very easy method of prayer] (1685)

NAME	PHONE (H)
ADDRESS	PHONE (W)
	FAX
EMAIL	CELL/PAGER

NAME	PHONE (H)
ADDRESS	PHONE (W)
	FAX
EMAIL	CELL/PAGER

NAME	PHONE (H)
ADDRESS	PHONE (W)
	FAX
EMAIL	CELL/PAGER

NAME	PHONE (H)
ADDRESS	PHONE (W)
	FAX
EMAIL	CELL/PAGER

NAME	PHONE (H)
ADDRESS	PHONE (W)
	FAX
EMAIL	CELL/PAGER

NAME	PHONE (H)
ADDRESS	PHONE (W)
	FAX
EMAIL	CELL/PAGER

NAME	PHONE (H)
ADDRESS	PHONE (W)
	FAX
EMAIL	CELL/PAGER

NAME	PHONE (H)
ADDRESS	PHONE (W)
	FAX
EMAIL	CELL/PAGER

NAME	PHONE (H)
ADDRESS	PHONE (W)
	FAX
EMAIL	CELL/PAGER

NAME	PHONE (H)
ADDRESS	PHONE (W)
	FAX
EMAIL	CELL/PAGER

NAME	PHONE (H)
ADDRESS	PHONE (W)
	FAX
EMAIL	CELL/PAGER

NAME	PHONE (H)
ADDRESS	PHONE (W)
	FAX
EMAIL	CELL/PAGER

NAME	PHONE (H)
ADDRESS	PHONE (W)
	FAX
EMAIL	CELL/PAGER

NAME	PHONE (H)
ADDRESS	PHONE (W)
	FAX
EMAIL	CELL/PAGER

NAME	PHONE (H)
ADDRESS	PHONE (W)
	FAX
EMAIL	CELL/PAGER

NAME	PHONE (H)
ADDRESS	PHONE (W)
	FAX
EMAIL	CELL/PAGER

NAME	PHONE (H)
ADDRESS	PHONE (W)
	FAX
EMAIL	CELL/PAGER

NAME	PHONE (H)
ADDRESS	PHONE (W)
	FAX
EMAIL	CELL/PAGER

NAME	PHONE (H)
ADDRESS	PHONE (W)
	FAX
EMAIL	CELL/PAGER

NAME	PHONE (H)
ADDRESS	PHONE (W)
	FAX
EMAIL	CELL/PAGER

NAME	PHONE (H)
ADDRESS	PHONE (W)
	FAX
EMAIL	CELL/PAGER

NAME	PHONE (H)
ADDRESS	PHONE (W)
	FAX
EMAIL	CELL/PAGER

NAME	PHONE (H)
ADDRESS	PHONE (W)
	FAX
EMAIL	CELL/PAGER

NAME	PHONE (H)
ADDRESS	PHONE (W)
	FAX
EMAIL	CELL/PAGER

Robert Hope (English, 1869–1936)
The Yellow Silk Dress, n.d.
Oil on canvas
Private collection
Photograph courtesy Bourne Gallery, Surrey, England / The Bridgeman Art Library, New York

> *There are books I go to when I don't want any more of the place I'm somehow stuck in and I long for a lighter*
> *and brighter world. . . . They make me feel I've just had a drink of a particularly sparkling Champagne.*
> —Mary Gordon (b. 1948)

Ignace Henri Jean Fantin-Latour (French, 1836–1904)
Reading, 1863
Oil on canvas
Musée des Beaux-Arts, Tournai, Belgium
Photograph courtesy Giraudon / The Bridgeman Art Library, New York

> *I only really love a book when I have read it at least four times.*
> —Nancy Spain, *A Funny Thing Happened on the Way* (1964)

NAME	PHONE (H)
ADDRESS	PHONE (W)
	FAX
EMAIL	CELL/PAGER

NAME	PHONE (H)
ADDRESS	PHONE (W)
	FAX
EMAIL	CELL/PAGER

NAME	PHONE (H)
ADDRESS	PHONE (W)
	FAX
EMAIL	CELL/PAGER

NAME	PHONE (H)
ADDRESS	PHONE (W)
	FAX
EMAIL	CELL/PAGER

NAME	PHONE (H)
ADDRESS	PHONE (W)
	FAX
EMAIL	CELL/PAGER

NAME	PHONE (H)
ADDRESS	PHONE (W)
	FAX
EMAIL	CELL/PAGER

NAME	PHONE (H)
ADDRESS	PHONE (W)
	FAX
EMAIL	CELL/PAGER

NAME	PHONE (H)
ADDRESS	PHONE (W)
	FAX .
EMAIL	CELL/PAGER

NAME	PHONE (H)
ADDRESS	PHONE (W)
	FAX
EMAIL	CELL/PAGER

NAME	PHONE (H)
ADDRESS	PHONE (W)
	FAX
EMAIL	CELL/PAGER

NAME	PHONE (H)
ADDRESS	PHONE (W)
	FAX
EMAIL	CELL/PAGER

NAME	PHONE (H)
ADDRESS	PHONE (W)
	FAX
EMAIL	CELL/PAGER

NAME	PHONE (H)
ADDRESS	PHONE (W)
	FAX
EMAIL	CELL/PAGER

NAME	PHONE (H)
ADDRESS	PHONE (W)
	FAX
EMAIL	CELL/PAGER

NAME	PHONE (H)
ADDRESS	PHONE (W)
	FAX
EMAIL	CELL/PAGER

NAME	PHONE (H)
ADDRESS	PHONE (W)
	FAX
EMAIL	CELL/PAGER

NAME	PHONE (H)
ADDRESS	PHONE (W)
	FAX
EMAIL	CELL/PAGER

NAME	PHONE (H)
ADDRESS	PHONE (W)
	FAX
EMAIL	CELL/PAGER

NAME	PHONE (H)
ADDRESS	PHONE (W)
	FAX
EMAIL	CELL/PAGER

NAME	PHONE (H)
ADDRESS	PHONE (W)
	FAX
EMAIL	CELL/PAGER

NAME	PHONE (H)
ADDRESS	PHONE (W)
	FAX
EMAIL	CELL/PAGER

NAME	PHONE (H)
ADDRESS	PHONE (W)
	FAX
EMAIL	CELL/PAGER

NAME	PHONE (H)
ADDRESS	PHONE (W)
	FAX
EMAIL	CELL/PAGER

NAME	PHONE (H)
ADDRESS	PHONE (W)
	FAX
EMAIL	CELL/PAGER

Frederic, Lord Leighton (English, 1830–1896)
The Maid with the Golden Hair, c. 1895
Private collection
Photograph courtesy Christie's Images, London / The Bridgeman Art Library, New York

What a sense of superiority it gives one to escape reading some book which every one else is reading.

—Alice James, attributed

William Hatherell (English, 1855–1928)
A Quiet Spot, 1891
Watercolor, 30.5 x 49.5 cm (12 x 19½ in.)
Private collection
© Christie's Images, London / The Bridgeman Art Library, New York

The greatest gift is the passion for reading. It is cheap, it consoles, it distracts,
it excites, it gives you knowledge of the world and
experience of a wide kind. It is a moral illumination.
—Elizabeth Hardwick

NAME	PHONE (H)
ADDRESS	PHONE (W)
	FAX
EMAIL	CELL/PAGER
NAME	PHONE (H)
ADDRESS	PHONE (W)
	FAX
EMAIL	CELL/PAGER
NAME	PHONE (H)
ADDRESS	PHONE (W)
	FAX
EMAIL	CELL/PAGER
NAME	PHONE (H)
ADDRESS	PHONE (W)
	FAX
EMAIL	CELL/PAGER
NAME	PHONE (H)
ADDRESS	PHONE (W)
	FAX
EMAIL	CELL/PAGER
NAME	PHONE (H)
ADDRESS	PHONE (W)
	FAX
EMAIL	CELL/PAGER

NAME	PHONE (H)
ADDRESS	PHONE (W)
	FAX
EMAIL	CELL/PAGER

NAME	PHONE (H)
ADDRESS	PHONE (W)
	FAX
EMAIL	CELL/PAGER

NAME	PHONE (H)
ADDRESS	PHONE (W)
	FAX
EMAIL	CELL/PAGER

NAME	PHONE (H)
ADDRESS	PHONE (W)
	FAX
EMAIL	CELL/PAGER

NAME	PHONE (H)
ADDRESS	PHONE (W)
	FAX
EMAIL	CELL/PAGER

NAME	PHONE (H)
ADDRESS	PHONE (W)
	FAX
EMAIL	CELL/PAGER

NAME

ADDRESS

EMAIL

PHONE (H)

PHONE (W)

FAX

CELL/PAGER

NAME

ADDRESS

EMAIL

PHONE (H)

PHONE (W)

FAX

CELL/PAGER

NAME

ADDRESS

EMAIL

PHONE (H)

PHONE (W)

FAX

CELL/PAGER

NAME

ADDRESS

EMAIL

PHONE (H)

PHONE (W)

FAX

CELL/PAGER

NAME

ADDRESS

EMAIL

PHONE (H)

PHONE (W)

FAX

CELL/PAGER

NAME

ADDRESS

EMAIL

PHONE (H)

PHONE (W)

FAX

CELL/PAGER

NAME	PHONE (H)
ADDRESS	PHONE (W)
	FAX
EMAIL	CELL/PAGER

NAME	PHONE (H)
ADDRESS	PHONE (W)
	FAX
EMAIL	CELL/PAGER

NAME	PHONE (H)
ADDRESS	PHONE (W)
	FAX
EMAIL	CELL/PAGER

NAME	PHONE (H)
ADDRESS	PHONE (W)
	FAX
EMAIL	CELL/PAGER

NAME	PHONE (H)
ADDRESS	PHONE (W)
	FAX
EMAIL	CELL/PAGER

NAME	PHONE (H)
ADDRESS	PHONE (W)
	FAX
EMAIL	CELL/PAGER

Hans Olaf Heyerdahl (Norwegian, 1857–1913)
At the Window, 1881
Oil on wood panel, 46 x 37 cm (18⅛ x 14⁹⁄₁₆ in.)
Nasjonalmuseet for kunst, arkitektur og design, Oslo
Photograph courtesy The Bridgeman Art Library, New York

Fiction reveals truth that reality obscures.
—Jessamyn West (1902–1984)

Jean-Baptiste-Camille Corot (French, 1796–1875)

The Reader Crowned with Flowers; or, Virgil's Muse, 1845

Oil on canvas, 47 x 34 cm (18½ x 13⅜ in.)

Musée du Louvre, Paris

Photograph courtesy Giraudon / The Bridgeman Art Library, New York

The true felicity of a lover of books is the luxurious turning of page by page, the surrender, not meanly abject, but delib-
erate and cautious, with your wits about you, as you deliver yourself into the keeping of a book. This I call reading.

—Edith Wharton, attributed

NAME	PHONE (H)
ADDRESS	PHONE (W)
	FAX
EMAIL	CELL/PAGER

NAME	PHONE (H)
ADDRESS	PHONE (W)
	FAX
EMAIL	CELL/PAGER

NAME	PHONE (H)
ADDRESS	PHONE (W)
	FAX
EMAIL	CELL/PAGER

NAME	PHONE (H)
ADDRESS	PHONE (W)
	FAX
EMAIL	CELL/PAGER

NAME	PHONE (H)
ADDRESS	PHONE (W)
	FAX
EMAIL	CELL/PAGER

NAME	PHONE (H)
ADDRESS	PHONE (W)
	FAX
EMAIL	CELL/PAGER

NAME | PHONE (H)

ADDRESS | PHONE (W)

| FAX

EMAIL | CELL/PAGER

NAME | PHONE (H)

ADDRESS | PHONE (W)

| FAX

EMAIL | CELL/PAGER

NAME | PHONE (H)

ADDRESS | PHONE (W)

| FAX

EMAIL | CELL/PAGER

NAME | PHONE (H)

ADDRESS | PHONE (W)

| FAX

EMAIL | CELL/PAGER

NAME | PHONE (H)

ADDRESS | PHONE (W)

| FAX

EMAIL | CELL/PAGER

NAME | PHONE (H)

ADDRESS | PHONE (W)

| FAX

EMAIL | CELL/PAGER

NAME	PHONE (H)
ADDRESS	PHONE (W)
	FAX
EMAIL	CELL/PAGER

NAME	PHONE (H)
ADDRESS	PHONE (W)
	FAX
EMAIL	CELL/PAGER

NAME	PHONE (H)
ADDRESS	PHONE (W)
	FAX
EMAIL	CELL/PAGER

NAME	PHONE (H)
ADDRESS	PHONE (W)
	FAX
EMAIL	CELL/PAGER

NAME	PHONE (H)
ADDRESS	PHONE (W)
	FAX
EMAIL	CELL/PAGER

NAME	PHONE (H)
ADDRESS	PHONE (W)
	FAX
EMAIL	CELL/PAGER

NAME	PHONE (H)
ADDRESS	PHONE (W)
	FAX
EMAIL	CELL/PAGER

NAME	PHONE (H)
ADDRESS	PHONE (W)
	FAX
EMAIL	CELL/PAGER

NAME	PHONE (H)
ADDRESS	PHONE (W)
	FAX
EMAIL	CELL/PAGER

NAME	PHONE (H)
ADDRESS	PHONE (W)
	FAX
EMAIL	CELL/PAGER

NAME	PHONE (H)
ADDRESS	PHONE (W)
	FAX
EMAIL	CELL/PAGER

NAME	PHONE (H)
ADDRESS	PHONE (W)
	FAX
EMAIL	CELL/PAGER

The greatest pleasures of reading consist in rereading.
—Vernon Lee, "Reading Books," *Hortus Vitae* (1904)

Peter Kraemer (German, 1823–1907)
Reading the Letter [Reverie], 1887
Oil on panel, 35.6 x 28 cm (14 x 11 in.)
Josef Mensing Gallery, Hamm-Rhynern, Germany
Photograph courtesy The Bridgeman Art Library, New York

Soon enough I had an opportunity to read my letter: my aunt fell asleep as was her wont, my uncle sat down at the harp-
sichord, my mother began a game of piquet with M. de Lisieux and M. Darlet, and I asked whether I might take a walk in
the garden, pleading a headache. Permission was granted. . . . I rushed to the large path leading to the fields and opened
the letter that follows: "No longer, my beautiful cousin, can I conceal from you the power that you have over me. . . ."
—Louise Tardieu d'Esclavelles, marquise d'Épinay, *Histoire de Madame de Montbrillant* (1770)

NAME	PHONE (H)
ADDRESS	PHONE (W)
	FAX
EMAIL	CELL/PAGER

NAME	PHONE (H)
ADDRESS	PHONE (W)
	FAX
EMAIL	CELL/PAGER

NAME	PHONE (H)
ADDRESS	PHONE (W)
	FAX
EMAIL	CELL/PAGER

NAME	PHONE (H)
ADDRESS	PHONE (W)
	FAX
EMAIL	CELL/PAGER

NAME	PHONE (H)
ADDRESS	PHONE (W)
	FAX
EMAIL	CELL/PAGER

NAME	PHONE (H)
ADDRESS	PHONE (W)
	FAX
EMAIL	CELL/PAGER

NAME

ADDRESS

EMAIL

PHONE (H)

PHONE (W)

FAX

CELL/PAGER

NAME

ADDRESS

EMAIL

PHONE (H)

PHONE (W)

FAX

CELL/PAGER

NAME

ADDRESS

EMAIL

PHONE (H)

PHONE (W)

FAX

CELL/PAGER

NAME

ADDRESS

EMAIL

PHONE (H)

PHONE (W)

FAX

CELL/PAGER

NAME

ADDRESS

EMAIL

PHONE (H)

PHONE (W)

FAX

CELL/PAGER

NAME

ADDRESS

EMAIL

PHONE (H)

PHONE (W)

FAX

CELL/PAGER

NAME	PHONE (H)
ADDRESS	PHONE (W)
	FAX
EMAIL	CELL/PAGER

NAME	PHONE (H)
ADDRESS	PHONE (W)
	FAX
EMAIL	CELL/PAGER

NAME	PHONE (H)
ADDRESS	PHONE (W)
	FAX
EMAIL	CELL/PAGER

NAME	PHONE (H)
ADDRESS	PHONE (W)
	FAX
EMAIL	CELL/PAGER

NAME	PHONE (H)
ADDRESS	PHONE (W)
	FAX
EMAIL	CELL/PAGER

NAME	PHONE (H)
ADDRESS	PHONE (W)
	FAX
EMAIL	CELL/PAGER

NAME	PHONE (H)
ADDRESS	PHONE (W)
	FAX
EMAIL	CELL/PAGER

NAME	PHONE (H)
ADDRESS	PHONE (W)
	FAX
EMAIL	CELL/PAGER

NAME	PHONE (H)
ADDRESS	PHONE (W)
	FAX
EMAIL	CELL/PAGER

NAME	PHONE (H)
ADDRESS	PHONE (W)
	FAX
EMAIL	CELL/PAGER

NAME	PHONE (H)
ADDRESS	PHONE (W)
	FAX
EMAIL	CELL/PAGER

NAME	PHONE (H)
ADDRESS	PHONE (W)
	FAX
EMAIL	CELL/PAGER

Gwendolyn Grant (Australian, 1878–1968)

Winter Sunshine, 1939

Oil on canvas, 71.8 x 61.5 cm (28¼ x 24³⁄₁₆ in.)

Private collection

Photograph courtesy The Bridgeman Art Library, New York

People say that life is the thing, but I prefer reading!
—Logan Pearsall Smith, *Afterthoughts* (1931)

George Dunlop Leslie (English, 1835–1921)
Alice in Wonderland, c. 1879
Oil on canvas, 81.4 x 111.8 cm (32¹/₁₆ x 44 in.)
Royal Pavilion, Libraries & Museums, Brighton & Hove, England
Photograph courtesy The Bridgeman Art Library, New York

Alice was beginning to get very tired of sitting by her sister on the bank and of having nothing to do:
once or twice she had peeped into the book her sister was reading, but it had no pictures or conversations in it,
"and what is the use of a book," thought Alice, "without pictures or conversations?"
—Lewis Carroll, *Alice's Adventures in Wonderland* (1865)

NAME	PHONE (H)
ADDRESS	PHONE (W)
	FAX
EMAIL	CELL/PAGER

NAME	PHONE (H)
ADDRESS	PHONE (W)
	FAX
EMAIL	CELL/PAGER

NAME	PHONE (H)
ADDRESS	PHONE (W)
	FAX
EMAIL	CELL/PAGER

NAME	PHONE (H)
ADDRESS	PHONE (W)
	FAX
EMAIL	CELL/PAGER

NAME	PHONE (H)
ADDRESS	PHONE (W)
	FAX
EMAIL	CELL/PAGER

NAME	PHONE (H)
ADDRESS	PHONE (W)
	FAX
EMAIL	CELL/PAGER

NAME	PHONE (H)
ADDRESS	PHONE (W)
	FAX
EMAIL	CELL/PAGER

NAME	PHONE (H)
ADDRESS	PHONE (W)
	FAX
EMAIL	CELL/PAGER

NAME	PHONE (H)
ADDRESS	PHONE (W)
	FAX
EMAIL	CELL/PAGER

NAME	PHONE (H)
ADDRESS	PHONE (W)
	FAX
EMAIL	CELL/PAGER

NAME	PHONE (H)
ADDRESS	PHONE (W)
	FAX
EMAIL	CELL/PAGER

NAME	PHONE (H)
ADDRESS	PHONE (W)
	FAX
EMAIL	CELL/PAGER

NAME	PHONE (H)
ADDRESS	PHONE (W)
	FAX
EMAIL	CELL/PAGER

NAME	PHONE (H)
ADDRESS	PHONE (W)
	FAX
EMAIL	CELL/PAGER

NAME	PHONE (H)
ADDRESS	PHONE (W)
	FAX
EMAIL	CELL/PAGER

NAME	PHONE (H)
ADDRESS	PHONE (W)
	FAX
EMAIL	CELL/PAGER

NAME	PHONE (H)
ADDRESS	PHONE (W)
	FAX
EMAIL	CELL/PAGER

NAME	PHONE (H)
ADDRESS	PHONE (W)
	FAX
EMAIL	CELL/PAGER

NAME

PHONE (H)

ADDRESS

PHONE (W)

FAX

EMAIL

CELL/PAGER

NAME

PHONE (H)

ADDRESS

PHONE (W)

FAX

EMAIL

CELL/PAGER

NAME

PHONE (H)

ADDRESS

PHONE (W)

FAX

EMAIL

CELL/PAGER

NAME

PHONE (H)

ADDRESS

PHONE (W)

FAX

EMAIL

CELL/PAGER

NAME

PHONE (H)

ADDRESS

PHONE (W)

FAX

EMAIL

CELL/PAGER

NAME

PHONE (H)

ADDRESS

PHONE (W)

FAX

EMAIL

CELL/PAGER

Jan Vermeer (Dutch, 1632–1675)
Woman Reading a Letter, c. 1662–1663
Oil on canvas, 46.5 x 39 cm (18⁵⁄₁₆ x 15³⁄₈ in.)
Rijksmuseum, Amsterdam
Photograph courtesy The Bridgeman Art Library, New York

> *The words loved me and I loved them in return.*
> —Sonia Sanchez, *Under a Soprano Sky* (1987)

Karl Maria Schuster (Austrian, 1871–1953)
Reading on the Terrace, Capri, 1904
Oil on canvas, 90.2 x 128.3 cm (35½ x 50½ in.)
Private collection
Photograph courtesy Waterhouse and Dodd, London / The Bridgeman Art Library, New York

To love these Books, and harmless Tea,
Has always been my foible,
Yet will I ne'er forgetful be
To read my Psalms and Bible
—Christian Ross Milne, "To a Lady Who Said It Was Sinful to Read Novels,"
in *Simple Poems on Simple Subjects* (1805)

NAME	PHONE (H)
ADDRESS	PHONE (W)
	FAX
EMAIL	CELL/PAGER

NAME	PHONE (H)
ADDRESS	PHONE (W)
	FAX
EMAIL	CELL/PAGER

NAME	PHONE (H)
ADDRESS	PHONE (W)
	FAX
EMAIL	CELL/PAGER

NAME	PHONE (H)
ADDRESS	PHONE (W)
	FAX
EMAIL	CELL/PAGER

NAME	PHONE (H)
ADDRESS	PHONE (W)
	FAX
EMAIL	CELL/PAGER

NAME	PHONE (H)
ADDRESS	PHONE (W)
	FAX
EMAIL	CELL/PAGER

NAME

ADDRESS

EMAIL

PHONE (H)

PHONE (W)

FAX

CELL/PAGER

NAME

ADDRESS

EMAIL

PHONE (H)

PHONE (W)

FAX

CELL/PAGER

NAME

ADDRESS

EMAIL

PHONE (H)

PHONE (W)

FAX

CELL/PAGER

NAME

ADDRESS

EMAIL

PHONE (H)

PHONE (W)

FAX

CELL/PAGER

NAME

ADDRESS

EMAIL

PHONE (H)

PHONE (W)

FAX

CELL/PAGER

NAME

ADDRESS

EMAIL

PHONE (H)

PHONE (W)

FAX

CELL/PAGER

NAME	PHONE (H)
ADDRESS	PHONE (W)
	FAX
EMAIL	CELL/PAGER

NAME	PHONE (H)
ADDRESS	PHONE (W)
	FAX
EMAIL	CELL/PAGER

NAME	PHONE (H)
ADDRESS	PHONE (W)
	FAX
EMAIL	CELL/PAGER

NAME	PHONE (H)
ADDRESS	PHONE (W)
	FAX
EMAIL	CELL/PAGER

NAME	PHONE (H)
ADDRESS	PHONE (W)
	FAX
EMAIL	CELL/PAGER

NAME	PHONE (H)
ADDRESS	PHONE (W)
	FAX
EMAIL	CELL/PAGER

NAME	PHONE (H)
ADDRESS	PHONE (W)
	FAX
EMAIL	CELL/PAGER

NAME	PHONE (H)
ADDRESS	PHONE (W)
	FAX
EMAIL	CELL/PAGER

NAME	PHONE (H)
ADDRESS	PHONE (W)
	FAX
EMAIL	CELL/PAGER

NAME	PHONE (H)
ADDRESS	PHONE (W)
	FAX
EMAIL	CELL/PAGER

NAME	PHONE (H)
ADDRESS	PHONE (W)
	FAX
EMAIL	CELL/PAGER

NAME	PHONE (H)
ADDRESS	PHONE (W)
	FAX
EMAIL	CELL/PAGER

Sir Edward John Poynter (English, 1836–1919)
Reading, 1871
Oil on canvas
Private collection
© Christie's Images, London / The Bridgeman Art Library, New York

*Persons still living remember a woman in Strathspey, who, though never taught to read, could recite
the whole book of Psalms in the Gaelic translation, merely by having it read to her by others. This to be sure
was the employment and delight of all the leisure hours of a long life; but it is a proof what hold
the memory takes, where the heart is deeply interested.*
—Anne MacVicar Grant, *Poems on Various Subjects* (1803)

Alexander Mann (Scottish, 1853–1908)
Portrait of Helen Gow, n.d.
Private collection
© The Fine Art Society, London / The Bridgeman Art Library, New York

Reading gives us someplace to go when we have to stay where we are.
—Mason Cooley (1927–2002)

NAME	PHONE (H)
ADDRESS	PHONE (W)
	FAX
EMAIL	CELL/PAGER

NAME	PHONE (H)
ADDRESS	PHONE (W)
	FAX
EMAIL	CELL/PAGER

NAME	PHONE (H)
ADDRESS	PHONE (W)
	FAX
EMAIL	CELL/PAGER

NAME	PHONE (H)
ADDRESS	PHONE (W)
	FAX
EMAIL	CELL/PAGER

NAME	PHONE (H)
ADDRESS	PHONE (W)
	FAX
EMAIL	CELL/PAGER

NAME	PHONE (H)
ADDRESS	PHONE (W)
	FAX
EMAIL	CELL/PAGER

NAME	PHONE (H)
ADDRESS	PHONE (W)
	FAX
EMAIL	CELL/PAGER

NAME	PHONE (H)
ADDRESS	PHONE (W)
	FAX
EMAIL	CELL/PAGER

NAME	PHONE (H)
ADDRESS	PHONE (W)
	FAX
EMAIL	CELL/PAGER

NAME	PHONE (H)
ADDRESS	PHONE (W)
	FAX
EMAIL	CELL/PAGER

NAME	PHONE (H)
ADDRESS	PHONE (W)
	FAX
EMAIL	CELL/PAGER

NAME	PHONE (H)
ADDRESS	PHONE (W)
	FAX
EMAIL	CELL/PAGER

NAME

ADDRESS

EMAIL

PHONE (H)

PHONE (W)

FAX

CELL/PAGER

NAME

ADDRESS

EMAIL

PHONE (H)

PHONE (W)

FAX

CELL/PAGER

NAME

ADDRESS

EMAIL

PHONE (H)

PHONE (W)

FAX

CELL/PAGER

NAME

ADDRESS

EMAIL

PHONE (H)

PHONE (W)

FAX

CELL/PAGER

NAME

ADDRESS

EMAIL

PHONE (H)

PHONE (W)

FAX

CELL/PAGER

NAME

ADDRESS

EMAIL

PHONE (H)

PHONE (W)

FAX

CELL/PAGER

NAME

ADDRESS

EMAIL

PHONE (H)

PHONE (W)

FAX

CELL/PAGER

NAME

ADDRESS

EMAIL

PHONE (H)

PHONE (W)

FAX

CELL/PAGER

NAME

ADDRESS

EMAIL

PHONE (H)

PHONE (W)

FAX

CELL/PAGER

NAME

ADDRESS

EMAIL

PHONE (H)

PHONE (W)

FAX

CELL/PAGER

NAME

ADDRESS

EMAIL

PHONE (H)

PHONE (W)

FAX

CELL/PAGER

NAME

ADDRESS

EMAIL

PHONE (H)

PHONE (W)

FAX

CELL/PAGER

Frank Dicey (English, fl. 1880–1888)

The Novel, c. 1880

Oil on panel, 39.4 x 52.1 cm (15½ x 20½ in.)

Private collection

© Christopher Wood Gallery, London / The Bridgeman Art Library, New York

Life being very short, and the quiet hours of it few, we ought to waste none of them
in reading valueless books. . . . Valuable books should, in a civilized country,
be within the reach of every one, printed in excellent form, for a just price. . . .
—John Ruskin, "The Mystery of Life," in *Sesame and Lilies* (1868)

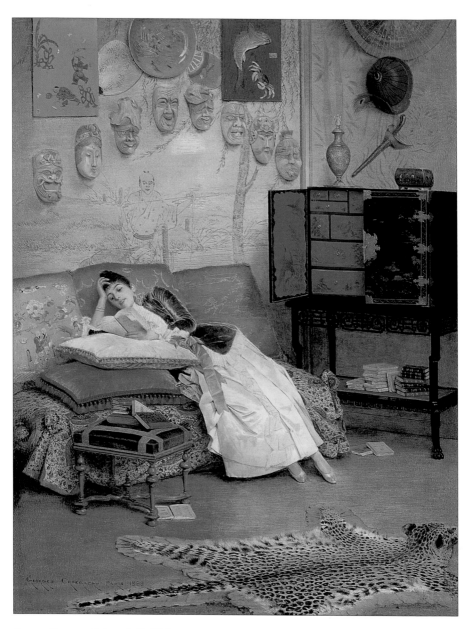

Georges Croegaert (Belgian, 1848–1923)

La liseuse, n.d.

Photograph courtesy Roy Miles Fine Paintings, London / The Bridgeman Art Library, New York

We should read to give our souls a chance to luxuriate.

—Henry Miller, attributed

NAME

ADDRESS

EMAIL

PHONE (H)

PHONE (W)

FAX

CELL/PAGER

NAME

ADDRESS

EMAIL

PHONE (H)

PHONE (W)

FAX

CELL/PAGER

NAME

ADDRESS

EMAIL

PHONE (H)

PHONE (W)

FAX

CELL/PAGER

NAME

ADDRESS

EMAIL

PHONE (H)

PHONE (W)

FAX

CELL/PAGER

NAME

ADDRESS

EMAIL

PHONE (H)

PHONE (W)

FAX

CELL/PAGER

NAME

ADDRESS

EMAIL

PHONE (H)

PHONE (W)

FAX

CELL/PAGER

NAME	PHONE (H)
ADDRESS	PHONE (W)
	FAX
EMAIL	CELL/PAGER

NAME	PHONE (H)
ADDRESS	PHONE (W)
	FAX
EMAIL	CELL/PAGER

NAME	PHONE (H)
ADDRESS	PHONE (W)
	FAX
EMAIL	CELL/PAGER

NAME	PHONE (H)
ADDRESS	PHONE (W)
	FAX
EMAIL	CELL/PAGER

NAME	PHONE (H)
ADDRESS	PHONE (W)
	FAX
EMAIL	CELL/PAGER

NAME	PHONE (H)
ADDRESS	PHONE (W)
	FAX
EMAIL	CELL/PAGER

NAME

ADDRESS

EMAIL

PHONE (H)

PHONE (W)

FAX

CELL/PAGER

NAME

ADDRESS

EMAIL

PHONE (H)

PHONE (W)

FAX

CELL/PAGER

NAME

ADDRESS

EMAIL

PHONE (H)

PHONE (W)

FAX

CELL/PAGER

NAME

ADDRESS

EMAIL

PHONE (H)

PHONE (W)

FAX

CELL/PAGER

NAME

ADDRESS

EMAIL

PHONE (H)

PHONE (W)

FAX

CELL/PAGER

NAME

ADDRESS

EMAIL

PHONE (H)

PHONE (W)

FAX

CELL/PAGER

NAME	PHONE (H)
ADDRESS	PHONE (W)
	FAX
EMAIL	CELL/PAGER

NAME	PHONE (H)
ADDRESS	PHONE (W)
	FAX
EMAIL	CELL/PAGER

NAME	PHONE (H)
ADDRESS	PHONE (W)
	FAX
EMAIL	CELL/PAGER

NAME	PHONE (H)
ADDRESS	PHONE (W)
	FAX
EMAIL	CELL/PAGER

NAME	PHONE (H)
ADDRESS	PHONE (W)
	FAX
EMAIL	CELL/PAGER

NAME	PHONE (H)
ADDRESS	PHONE (W)
	FAX
EMAIL	CELL/PAGER

Pierre-Auguste Renoir (French, 1841–1919)
Woman Reading, c. 1900
Oil on canvas, 56 x 46 cm (22⅕⁄₁₆ x 18⅛ in.)
© Tokyo Fuji Art Museum, Tokyo
Photograph courtesy The Bridgeman Art Library, New York

There are perhaps no days of our childhood that we lived as fully as those
we imagined we had not lived at all: those we spent with a beloved book.
—Marcel Proust, *Sur la lecture* (1905)

Peder Severin Krøyer (Danish, 1851–1909)
Roses; or, The Artist's Wife in the Garden at Skagen, 1893
Oil on canvas
Private collection
© The Fine Art Society, London / The Bridgeman Art Library, New York

Sunday Morning 14th [September 1800]. Made bread. A sore thumb from a cut. A lovely day—read
Boswell in the house in the morning and after dinner under the bright yellow leaves of the orchard.
The pear trees a bright yellow, the apple trees green still. A sweet lovely afternoon.
—Dorothy Wordsworth, *The Grasmere Journals,* in *Journals of Dorothy Wordsworth* (1971)

NAME	PHONE (H)
ADDRESS	PHONE (W)
	FAX
EMAIL	CELL/PAGER

NAME	PHONE (H)
ADDRESS	PHONE (W)
	FAX
EMAIL	CELL/PAGER

NAME	PHONE (H)
ADDRESS	PHONE (W)
	FAX
EMAIL	CELL/PAGER

NAME	PHONE (H)
ADDRESS	PHONE (W)
	FAX
EMAIL	CELL/PAGER

NAME	PHONE (H)
ADDRESS	PHONE (W)
	FAX
EMAIL	CELL/PAGER

NAME	PHONE (H)
ADDRESS	PHONE (W)
	FAX
EMAIL	CELL/PAGER

NAME	PHONE (H)
ADDRESS	PHONE (W)
	FAX
EMAIL	CELL/PAGER

NAME	PHONE (H)
ADDRESS	PHONE (W)
	FAX
EMAIL	CELL/PAGER

NAME	PHONE (H)
ADDRESS	PHONE (W)
	FAX
EMAIL	CELL/PAGER

NAME	PHONE (H)
ADDRESS	PHONE (W)
	FAX
EMAIL	CELL/PAGER

NAME	PHONE (H)
ADDRESS	PHONE (W)
	FAX
EMAIL	CELL/PAGER

NAME	PHONE (H)
ADDRESS	PHONE (W)
	FAX
EMAIL	CELL/PAGER

NAME	PHONE (H)
ADDRESS	PHONE (W)
	FAX
EMAIL	CELL/PAGER

NAME	PHONE (H)
ADDRESS	PHONE (W)
	FAX
EMAIL	CELL/PAGER

NAME	PHONE (H)
ADDRESS	PHONE (W)
	FAX
EMAIL	CELL/PAGER

NAME	PHONE (H)
ADDRESS	PHONE (W)
	FAX
EMAIL	CELL/PAGER

NAME	PHONE (H)
ADDRESS	PHONE (W)
	FAX
EMAIL	CELL/PAGER

NAME	PHONE (H)
ADDRESS	PHONE (W)
	FAX
EMAIL	CELL/PAGER

NAME	PHONE (H)
ADDRESS	PHONE (W)
	FAX
EMAIL	CELL/PAGER

NAME	PHONE (H)
ADDRESS	PHONE (W)
	FAX
EMAIL	CELL/PAGER

NAME	PHONE (H)
ADDRESS	PHONE (W)
	FAX
EMAIL	CELL/PAGER

NAME	PHONE (H)
ADDRESS	PHONE (W)
	FAX
EMAIL	CELL/PAGER

NAME	PHONE (H)
ADDRESS	PHONE (W)
	FAX
EMAIL	CELL/PAGER

NAME	PHONE (H)
ADDRESS	PHONE (W)
	FAX
EMAIL	CELL/PAGER

Peter Vilhelm Ilsted (Danish, 1861–1933)
Woman Reading by Candlelight, 1908
Oil on canvas, 47 x 38.5 cm (18½ x 15³⁄₁₆ in.)
Private collection
© Connaught Brown, London / The Bridgeman Art Library, New York

Literature is my Utopia. Here I am not disenfranchised. No barrier of the senses shuts me out from the sweet,
gracious discourse of my book-friends. They talk to me without embarrassment or awkwardness.
—Helen Keller (1880–1968)

Pierre-Auguste Renoir (French, 1841–1919)

Young Girl Reading, 1897

Oil on canvas, 40.5 x 28.5 cm (15¹⁵⁄₁₆ x 11¼ in.)

Private collection

© Lefevre Fine Art Ltd., London / The Bridgeman Art Library, New York

When I was about eight, I decided that the most wonderful thing, next to a human being, was a book.
—Margaret Walker, quoted in Brian Lanker, *I Dream a World* (1989)

NAME

ADDRESS

EMAIL

PHONE (H)

PHONE (W)

FAX

CELL/PAGER

NAME

ADDRESS

EMAIL

PHONE (H)

PHONE (W)

FAX

CELL/PAGER

NAME

ADDRESS

EMAIL

PHONE (H)

PHONE (W)

FAX

CELL/PAGER

NAME

ADDRESS

EMAIL

PHONE (H)

PHONE (W)

FAX

CELL/PAGER

NAME

ADDRESS

EMAIL

PHONE (H)

PHONE (W)

FAX

CELL/PAGER

NAME

ADDRESS

EMAIL

PHONE (H)

PHONE (W)

FAX

CELL/PAGER

NAME

ADDRESS

EMAIL

PHONE (H)

PHONE (W)

FAX

CELL/PAGER

NAME

ADDRESS

EMAIL

PHONE (H)

PHONE (W)

FAX

CELL/PAGER

NAME

ADDRESS

EMAIL

PHONE (H)

PHONE (W)

FAX

CELL/PAGER

NAME

ADDRESS

EMAIL

PHONE (H)

PHONE (W)

FAX

CELL/PAGER

NAME

ADDRESS

EMAIL

PHONE (H)

PHONE (W)

FAX

CELL/PAGER

NAME

ADDRESS

EMAIL

PHONE (H)

PHONE (W)

FAX

CELL/PAGER

NAME	PHONE (H)
ADDRESS	PHONE (W)
	FAX
EMAIL	CELL/PAGER

NAME	PHONE (H)
ADDRESS	PHONE (W)
	FAX
EMAIL	CELL/PAGER

NAME	PHONE (H)
ADDRESS	PHONE (W)
	FAX
EMAIL	CELL/PAGER

NAME	PHONE (H)
ADDRESS	PHONE (W)
	FAX
EMAIL	CELL/PAGER

NAME	PHONE (H)
ADDRESS	PHONE (W)
	FAX
EMAIL	CELL/PAGER

NAME	PHONE (H)
ADDRESS	PHONE (W)
	FAX
EMAIL	CELL/PAGER

NAME	PHONE (H)
ADDRESS	PHONE (W)
	FAX
EMAIL	CELL/PAGER

NAME	PHONE (H)
ADDRESS	PHONE (W)
	FAX
EMAIL	CELL/PAGER

NAME	PHONE (H)
ADDRESS	PHONE (W)
	FAX
EMAIL	CELL/PAGER

NAME	PHONE (H)
ADDRESS	PHONE (W)
	FAX
EMAIL	CELL/PAGER

NAME	PHONE (H)
ADDRESS	PHONE (W)
	FAX
EMAIL	CELL/PAGER

NAME	PHONE (H)
ADDRESS	PHONE (W)
	FAX
EMAIL	CELL/PAGER

Jean-Baptiste-Armand Guillaumin (French, 1841–1927)
Madame Guillaumin Reading, c. 1887
Oil on canvas, 46.5 x 55 cm (18⁵⁄₁₆ x 21⁵⁄₈ in.)
Galerie Daniel Malingue, Paris
Photograph courtesy The Bridgeman Art Library, New York

Read the best books first, or you may not have a chance to read them at all.
—Henry David Thoreau (1817–1862)

Carl Vilhelm Holsøe (Danish, 1863–1935)
Woman Reading in a Sunlit Room, n.d.
Private collection
© Connaught Brown, London / The Bridgeman Art Library, New York

I do love secondhand books that open to the page some previous owner read oftenest.
—Helen Hanff, 84, Charing Cross Road (1970)

NAME	PHONE (H)
ADDRESS	PHONE (W)
	FAX
EMAIL	CELL/PAGER

NAME	PHONE (H)
ADDRESS	PHONE (W)
	FAX
EMAIL	CELL/PAGER

NAME	PHONE (H)
ADDRESS	PHONE (W)
	FAX
EMAIL	CELL/PAGER

NAME	PHONE (H)
ADDRESS	PHONE (W)
	FAX
EMAIL	CELL/PAGER

NAME	PHONE (H)
ADDRESS	PHONE (W)
	FAX
EMAIL	CELL/PAGER

NAME	PHONE (H)
ADDRESS	PHONE (W)
	FAX
EMAIL	CELL/PAGER

NAME	PHONE (H)
ADDRESS	PHONE (W)
	FAX
EMAIL	CELL/PAGER

NAME	PHONE (H)
ADDRESS	PHONE (W)
	FAX
EMAIL	CELL/PAGER

NAME	PHONE (H)
ADDRESS	PHONE (W)
	FAX
EMAIL	CELL/PAGER

NAME	PHONE (H)
ADDRESS	PHONE (W)
	FAX
EMAIL	CELL/PAGER

NAME	PHONE (H)
ADDRESS	PHONE (W)
	FAX
EMAIL	CELL/PAGER

NAME	PHONE (H)
ADDRESS	PHONE (W)
	FAX
EMAIL	CELL/PAGER

NAME	PHONE (H)
ADDRESS	PHONE (W)
	FAX
EMAIL	CELL/PAGER

NAME	PHONE (H)
ADDRESS	PHONE (W)
	FAX
EMAIL	CELL/PAGER

NAME	PHONE (H)
ADDRESS	PHONE (W)
	FAX
EMAIL	CELL/PAGER

NAME	PHONE (H)
ADDRESS	PHONE (W)
	FAX
EMAIL	CELL/PAGER

NAME	PHONE (H)
ADDRESS	PHONE (W)
	FAX
EMAIL	CELL/PAGER

NAME	PHONE (H)
ADDRESS	PHONE (W)
	FAX
EMAIL	CELL/PAGER

NAME		PHONE (H)	
ADDRESS		PHONE (W)	
		FAX	
EMAIL		CELL/PAGER	

NAME		PHONE (H)	
ADDRESS		PHONE (W)	
		FAX	
EMAIL		CELL/PAGER	

NAME		PHONE (H)	
ADDRESS		PHONE (W)	
		FAX	
EMAIL		CELL/PAGER	

NAME		PHONE (H)	
ADDRESS		PHONE (W)	
		FAX	
EMAIL		CELL/PAGER	

NAME		PHONE (H)	
ADDRESS		PHONE (W)	
		FAX	
EMAIL		CELL/PAGER	

NAME		PHONE (H)	
ADDRESS		PHONE (W)	
		FAX	
EMAIL		CELL/PAGER	

Harriet Backer (Norwegian, 1845–1932)

By Lamplight, 1890

Oil on canvas, 54.7 x 66.5 cm (21⁹⁄₁₆ x 26³⁄₁₆ in.)

Bergen Kunstmuseum, Rasmus Meyer Collection, Bergen, Norway

Photograph courtesy The Bridgeman Art Library, New York

I've never known any trouble that an hour's reading didn't assuage.

—Charles de Secondat (1689–1755)

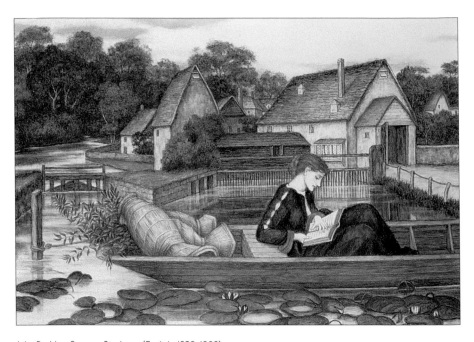

John Roddam Spencer Stanhope (English, 1829–1908)
The Mill
Watercolor
Private collection
© Bonhams, London / The Bridgeman Art Library, New York

From my earliest days, I loved everything about the sound, power and delivery of words.
—Phyllis Theroux

NAME	PHONE (H)
ADDRESS	PHONE (W)
	FAX
EMAIL	CELL/PAGER

NAME	PHONE (H)
ADDRESS	PHONE (W)
	FAX
EMAIL	CELL/PAGER

NAME	PHONE (H)
ADDRESS	PHONE (W)
	FAX
EMAIL	CELL/PAGER

NAME	PHONE (H)
ADDRESS	PHONE (W)
	FAX
EMAIL	CELL/PAGER

NAME	PHONE (H)
ADDRESS	PHONE (W)
	FAX
EMAIL	CELL/PAGER

NAME	PHONE (H)
ADDRESS	PHONE (W)
	FAX
EMAIL	CELL/PAGER

NAME	PHONE (H)
ADDRESS	PHONE (W)
	FAX
EMAIL	CELL/PAGER
NAME	PHONE (H)
ADDRESS	PHONE (W)
	FAX
EMAIL	CELL/PAGER
NAME	PHONE (H)
ADDRESS	PHONE (W)
	FAX
EMAIL	CELL/PAGER
NAME	PHONE (H)
ADDRESS	PHONE (W)
	FAX
EMAIL	CELL/PAGER
NAME	PHONE (H)
ADDRESS	PHONE (W)
	FAX
EMAIL	CELL/PAGER
NAME	PHONE (H)
ADDRESS	PHONE (W)
	FAX
EMAIL	CELL/PAGER

NAME	PHONE (H)
ADDRESS	PHONE (W)
	FAX
EMAIL	CELL/PAGER

NAME	PHONE (H)
ADDRESS	PHONE (W)
	FAX
EMAIL	CELL/PAGER

NAME	PHONE (H)
ADDRESS	PHONE (W)
	FAX
EMAIL	CELL/PAGER

NAME	PHONE (H)
ADDRESS	PHONE (W)
	FAX
EMAIL	CELL/PAGER

NAME	PHONE (H)
ADDRESS	PHONE (W)
	FAX
EMAIL	CELL/PAGER

NAME	PHONE (H)
ADDRESS	PHONE (W)
	FAX
EMAIL	CELL/PAGER

NAME	PHONE (H)
ADDRESS	PHONE (W)
	FAX
EMAIL	CELL/PAGER

NAME	PHONE (H)
ADDRESS	PHONE (W)
	FAX
EMAIL	CELL/PAGER

NAME	PHONE (H)
ADDRESS	PHONE (W)
	FAX
EMAIL	CELL/PAGER

NAME	PHONE (H)
ADDRESS	PHONE (W)
	FAX
EMAIL	CELL/PAGER

NAME	PHONE (H)
ADDRESS	PHONE (W)
	FAX
EMAIL	CELL/PAGER

NAME	PHONE (H)
ADDRESS	PHONE (W)
	FAX
EMAIL	CELL/PAGER

Valentine Cameron Prinsep (English, 1838–1904)

Lady Tennyson on Afton Downs, Freshwater Bay, Isle of Wight, n.d.

Private collection

© Mallett Gallery, London / The Bridgeman Art Library, New York

> *Properly, we should read for power. Man reading should be man intensely alive.*
> *The book should be a ball of light in one's hand.*
> —Ezra Pound, *Guide to Kulchur* (1938)

Maria Konstantinova Bashkirtseva (Ukrainian, 1860–1884)
At a Book, n.d.
Oil on canvas, 63 x 60 cm (24¹³/₁₆ x 23⅝ in.)
Kharkov Art Museum, Kharkov, Ukraine
Photograph courtesy The Bridgeman Art Library, New York

I am the most interesting book of all.
—Marie Bashkirtseff [Maria Konstantinova Bashkirtseva],
The Diary of Marie Bashkirtseff, trans. Mathilde Blind (1997)

NAME

ADDRESS

EMAIL

PHONE (H)

PHONE (W)

FAX

CELL/PAGER

NAME

ADDRESS

EMAIL

PHONE (H)

PHONE (W)

FAX

CELL/PAGER

NAME

ADDRESS

EMAIL

PHONE (H)

PHONE (W)

FAX

CELL/PAGER

NAME

ADDRESS

EMAIL

PHONE (H)

PHONE (W)

FAX

CELL/PAGER

NAME

ADDRESS

EMAIL

PHONE (H)

PHONE (W)

FAX

CELL/PAGER

NAME

ADDRESS

EMAIL

PHONE (H)

PHONE (W)

FAX

CELL/PAGER

NAME	PHONE (H)
ADDRESS	PHONE (W)
	FAX
EMAIL	CELL/PAGER

NAME	PHONE (H)
ADDRESS	PHONE (W)
	FAX
EMAIL	CELL/PAGER

NAME	PHONE (H)
ADDRESS	PHONE (W)
	FAX
EMAIL	CELL/PAGER

NAME	PHONE (H)
ADDRESS	PHONE (W)
	FAX
EMAIL	CELL/PAGER

NAME	PHONE (H)
ADDRESS	PHONE (W)
	FAX
EMAIL	CELL/PAGER

NAME	PHONE (H)
ADDRESS	PHONE (W)
	FAX
EMAIL	CELL/PAGER

NAME	PHONE (H)
ADDRESS	PHONE (W)
	FAX
EMAIL	CELL/PAGER

NAME	PHONE (H)
ADDRESS	PHONE (W)
	FAX
EMAIL	CELL/PAGER

NAME	PHONE (H)
ADDRESS	PHONE (W)
	FAX
EMAIL	CELL/PAGER

NAME	PHONE (H)
ADDRESS	PHONE (W)
	FAX
EMAIL	CELL/PAGER

NAME	PHONE (H)
ADDRESS	PHONE (W)
	FAX
EMAIL	CELL/PAGER

NAME	PHONE (H)
ADDRESS	PHONE (W)
	FAX
EMAIL	CELL/PAGER

NAME	PHONE (H)
ADDRESS	PHONE (W)
	FAX
EMAIL	CELL/PAGER

NAME	PHONE (H)
ADDRESS	PHONE (W)
	FAX
EMAIL	CELL/PAGER

NAME	PHONE (H)
ADDRESS	PHONE (W)
	FAX
EMAIL	CELL/PAGER

NAME	PHONE (H)
ADDRESS	PHONE (W)
	FAX
EMAIL	CELL/PAGER

NAME	PHONE (H)
ADDRESS	PHONE (W)
	FAX
EMAIL	CELL/PAGER

NAME	PHONE (H)
ADDRESS	PHONE (W)
	FAX
EMAIL	CELL/PAGER